CLIFTON

Why Build a Bridge?

THE Clifton Suspension Bridge, although not completed until 1864, owes its existence to the vision of a man who died over a century before – William Vick. Vick came to Bristol from Gloucestershire in the 1720s. Over the next 30 years he became a prosperous wine merchant who took a prominent part in city affairs, being made a Freeman in 1731. When he died in 1754 he left £1,000 to be invested until it became £10,000, when it was to be used to build a stone bridge across the Avon gorge linking Clifton Down near the city with Leigh Woods on the Somerset side.

It is something of a mystery where Vick got his notion from, for there was little development on either side of the gorge in his time. Clifton Down consisted mainly of open fields with only an ancient church, one or two farms and some houses dotted about. The Leigh Woods side was a mass of trees and little else.

In the last years of the 18th century, things were to change. Bristol entered a new era of prosperity. The wealthy moved from riverside houses at the foot of the gorge into elegant terraces newly built on the slopes above. Clifton became the fashionable place to live. Consequently interest in Vick's legacy revived.

In 1793, William Bridges published a grand design for a stone bridge with a huge central arch and five tiered galleries on either side to accommodate a variety of domestic, industrial and commercial activity. The crowning glory was to be a lighthouse and weather-vane.

Suddenly, in the same year, the bubble of prosperity burst. France began a war with England that was destined to continue for 22 years. Fears of invasion coupled with domestic unrest and economic decline put an end to most building projects. In Clifton 500 houses stood unfinished for many years.

OPPOSITE
The Avon gorge today, with the Severn estuary beyond.

BELOW
William Bridges' fanciful design of 1793. The galleries were to house units ranging from a granary to a corn exchange, a chapel to a tavern. There were to be engines and windmills for power and lamps for illumination.

In 1815 Napoleon was finally defeated at Waterloo. Within three years, the Avon gorge was once more thronged with ships and Bristol's city boundaries were expanding fast. Communication became the byword of the times. In 1826 Thomas Telford's Menai and Conway bridges captured the nation's imagination. The city fathers of Bristol looked on with interest and some concern at engineering achievements elsewhere. What is more, William Vick's legacy for a bridge at Clifton now totalled several thousand pounds.

LEFT
The Avon gorge *c.*1823, from a painting by Samuel Jackson.

A Competition Will be Held

PRESSURE in the city of Bristol mounted for a bridge to be built across the Avon gorge in fulfilment of William Vick's wish. With this firmly in mind, a committee was formed, consisting of the mayor and other prominent citizens.

Ships passing through the gorge en route from the sea to the docks required at least 30m (100 feet) clearance beneath a bridge, so any stone structure would have had to be massive indeed – one has only to look at William Bridges' design. Nevertheless, under the terms of Vick's will, the committee was obliged to do everything possible for a stone bridge. The members were therefore somewhat jolted to receive estimates of around £90,000 for the work. This clearly put a stone bridge out of the question, for the bequest was still worth only £8,000.

RIGHT
William Burge's 1830 design for a stone bridge.

BELOW
W.W. Young's competition entry. A stone bridge was to prove far too costly for the bridge committee to contemplate.

However, technical advances in recent years had made another material, wrought iron, worth considering. This had been invented in 1784 by Henry Cort. By heating iron with ferric oxide, he removed most of the carbon, making it less brittle than the older form of cast iron.

So the bridge committee fixed its sights on an iron suspension bridge, but the cost of even this type of bridge would be far in excess of the money from the Vick legacy. The only answer was to levy a toll on those people crossing the bridge, and in order to make this possible it was decided to seek an Act of Parliament.

Telford rejected the designs of all the remaining contenders, including Brunel, maintaining that 183m (600 feet) was the maximum admissible span. To complicate matters, he was asked to produce his own design for the new bridge. Perhaps not surprisingly, this was accepted in glowing terms by the committee and forwarded, in January 1830, with the Bill for parliamentary approval.

LEFT
William Butterfield, later to become famous as an architect of Gothic Revival buildings, was only 16 years of age when he submitted this competition entry.

On 1 October 1829 a competition to design a suspension bridge was announced, with a prize of 100 guineas offered to the winner. By late November, 22 sets of plans had been submitted and nearly all of them rejected, mostly on the grounds of appearance and cost rather than on technical merit. At this point the committee called in Thomas Telford to make the final selection. Although over 70 years old, Telford was the country's foremost civil engineer, whose Menai and Conway bridges had won national acclaim.

ABOVE
An unusual design submitted by Willam Hill of Bristol.

LEFT
Thomas Telford's late entry won over the committee but was reviled by the people of Bristol.

A Change of Plan

WHEN the Bill for Parliament was put forward, the company to build the bridge was formed and subscriptions invited. Problems immediately arose on two fronts. Firstly, Telford's design met with considerable criticism from both the public and disappointed competitors. Secondly, there was loud opposition from conservationists and ferry operators, who disliked the idea of any bridge at all. Although money from investors poured in during January, the flow slowed to a trickle in February and effectively dried up in March, some £22,000 short of the sum required for the construction alone.

Despite the problems, the Act of Parliament received royal assent in May 1830, giving a very detailed framework for the construction and administration of the bridge. Through summer into autumn the controversy continued until, at a meeting in October, the trustees decided to hold a second competition, for a bridge costing £40,000. At this point they tactfully set aside the Telford plan on grounds of cost.

RIGHT
I.K. Brunel's first design for the 1829 competition, the 'Giant's Hole', was reputedly his favourite.

BELOW
Brunel's second design incorporated a much-reduced span from his first concept.

The trustees were determined that the second competition should not suffer the deficiencies of the first. To this end they appointed as judge Davies Gilbert MP, an eminent scientist and engineer, assisted by John Seaward, a mathematician and an expert in iron-founding.

In the final stages of assessment, after much lobbying and public debate, only four schemes remained, those of J.M. Rendel, W. Hawks, Captain S. Brown and Isambard Kingdom Brunel, who had submitted four designs for consideration. Rendel's proposals were considered too expensive; Captain Brown's scheme involved an unacceptable stress on the chains.

LEFT
Like his previous design, Brunel's third involved the building of an abutment at the Leigh Woods end.

BELOW
Brunel's 'Egyptian thing', submitted in haste, was unanimously adopted by the 15 judges, reversing their decision to adopt W. Hawks's design.

On 16 March 1831, Gilbert and Seaward placed Brunel's efforts second behind those of Hawks, criticizing the chain design, the anchorage and the suspension rods. The young Brunel could not contain his frustration. Arming himself with copious drawings, he arranged a meeting with the judges and trustees. By the time he had finished, not only were the judges satisfied with the technical soundness of his plans, but his eloquence had persuaded the committee to accept his idea to decorate the suspension towers in Egyptian style. Thus the previous decision was reversed and Brunel's plans were unanimously adopted. Brunel was appointed civil engineer to the project. What Mr Hawks thought about this change of fortune is not recorded!

LEFT
Judging by the lack of detail, Brunel's heart was not in this effort, for he was confident that a longer span was required.

Brunel's final and winning design for Clifton Suspension Bridge, painted by Samuel Jackson in April 1831. The sphinxes are shown facing inwards, but Brunel soon realized that they would be more impressive if they faced approaching carriages.

Isambard Kingdom Brunel

BELOW
The famous picture of I.K. Brunel by the massive chains of his steamship, *Great Eastern.*

ISAMBARD Kingdom Brunel was a giant in an age of engineering giants. Clifton Suspension Bridge was his first and dearest individual commission – he called it 'My first child, my darling'. As well as being his passport to other great works, it led to a lifelong association with Bristol.

He was born in 1806, the son of Sir Marc Brunel, himself a renowned engineer. Such was Isambard's genius that he had mastered Euclid's mathematical works by the age of 6. At the age of 18 he took over the construction of the Thames Tunnel at Rotherhithe (the world's first underwater tunnel) after his father became ill with worry as a result of continual flooding and other problems. At 22, the young Brunel was almost killed when Thames water again burst into the tunnel. He was swept along but was thrown to the surface unconscious. Work on the tunnel halted for eight years.

But Isambard had great determination. After a period of recuperation, some of it spent at Clifton, he travelled the country seeking work – drainage in Essex, an observatory in Kensington, dock schemes in Sunderland and Bristol. Learning of the Clifton bridge competition, he sensed that this was the major commission he had been waiting for.

He diligently studied suspension bridges around the country and sounded out ideas with his father and fellow engineers. Finally he submitted no fewer than four designs (see pages VI and VII). The rest of the competition story we know.

After Clifton, Brunel went on to many fine achievements. His work in Bristol brought him into contact with the city's merchants, which led to his most famous commission. A railway was to be built between London and the West Country. The merchants, impressed with Brunel's way of working and his uncompromising insistence on quality, appointed him, in 1833, engineer to the new Great Western Railway. During the next 26 years he was to build 1,200 miles of railway incorporating many fine examples of his expertise and aesthetic judgement: Box Tunnel; Sonning Cutting; Paddington and Temple Meads stations; the Royal Albert Bridge at Saltash.

Brunel's other projects were many and varied. In 1841 he started work on the Hungerford suspension footbridge across the Thames, a project destined to play an unexpected part in the history of Clifton bridge after Brunel's death.

His career-long involvement with the sea by no means ended in dock construction. Half in jest, he suggested to the directors of the GWR that they extend their railway by building a steamship to cross the Atlantic. At the time this had never been

RIGHT
Brunel's crowning achievement was the creation of the Great Western Railway, from London to Bristol. Here the engine *Firefly*, depicted by Terence Cuneo, emerges from Box Tunnel, itself one of the greatest feats of civil engineering on the GWR.

achieved, but Brunel knew that a large vessel would be capable of it. The dream became reality on 8 April 1838 when the Bristol-built steamship *Great Western* sailed for New York. Unfortunately, neither this vessel nor its iron-hulled successor, SS *Great Britain*, was ever to achieve the success that was expected. Bristol's narrow docks proved unsuitable for big ships, although both vessels sailed profitably from Liverpool for many years. In 1970, amid emotional scenes, the *Great Britain* came back beneath Clifton Suspension Bridge to stand proudly in the dock where she was built.

Brunel was never to see his last steamship, the huge *Great Eastern* (211m/ 692 feet long), take to the ocean. On 5 September 1859 he suffered a stroke, four days before she left the Thames for trials. Ten days later he was dead, at the age of 53, worn out by a life of unremitting hard work.

ABOVE
Another of Brunel's achievements, the SS *Great Britain*, was built and launched in Bristol and is now berthed within a mile of Clifton Suspension Bridge.

RIGHT
The scene at 7 a.m. on 27 August 1836 when the bridge's foundation stone was laid by the Marquess of Northampton. The early hour was chosen to avoid disrupting river traffic.

FROM the outset, the building of Clifton Suspension Bridge was destined to be a slow and erratic process. Thirty-three years were to elapse between the start of the work and the first carriages travelling over the Avon gorge.

The first serious delay happened almost immediately after contracts were awarded. Despite a shortfall in capital of £20,000, and widespread social unrest in the country, a ceremonial start to the work was made on 21 June 1831 in the hope that interest in a live project would generate the necessary funds. Within days the Bristol riots* broke out and for weeks the whole city was in chaos. All work on the bridge stopped and Brunel found himself employed not as an engineer but as a special constable rescuing the city's treasures from the mob. Any traces of commercial optimism disappeared overnight. Subscriptions to the bridge halted abruptly. Five years were to go by before interest in the project was rekindled, thanks mainly to confidence engendered by the passage of the Great Western Railway Bill through Parliament.

Amidst crowded scenes, the stone to commence the Leigh abutment (the west pier of the bridge) was finally laid on 27 August 1836 by the Marquess of Northampton, President of the British Association for the Advancement of Science.

Over the next few years, work proceeded fairly steadily despite certain setbacks – the most significant being the bankruptcy in 1837 of the main contractors. From then on the trustees took over the work themselves and a motley collection of hard-drinking Cornish miners, Bristol masons and quarrymen set to work to shape the bridge's foundations. The rock used was old red sandstone quarried locally. By 1840 the Leigh abutment was completed, but at a cost of over £13,000.

The year 1843 was to prove a black one for the bridge. For some time the supporting piers had stood ready for the chains,

* The Reform Bill was designed to eliminate rotten boroughs, parliamentary seats with no proper constituency that were in the hands of the wealthy and well-connected. The Recorder of Bristol, Sir Charles Wetherall, an outspoken opponent of the Bill, was visiting the city at a time when the Bill was rejected for a second time by the Lords. His presence sparked off the riots.

excavations for the chain anchorages and approach roads were finished and some of the ironwork was on order. In February, to the surprise and consternation of everyone in Bristol, the trustees announced that the fund of £45,000 was used up and that, to complete the bridge, a further £30,000 would have to be found.

For the second time in its short history, work on the bridge stopped and the men were laid off. Efforts to raise money proved fruitless, for all around there were newer and potentially more lucrative ventures to tempt the investor, not the least of these being the Great Western Railway. To pay off clamouring creditors, the chains and plant were sold off in 1851 to become part of the Royal Albert Bridge, Saltash, another of Brunel's masterpieces. On 29 May 1853 the time limit set by Parliament expired and all work was abandoned. The piers in their rough, unfinished state stood gaunt on the cliffs, unheeded except by those who campaigned for their demolition.

When work on the bridge started in 1836, an iron bar 307m (1,000 feet) long and 3cm (1.25 inches) in diameter had been drawn by capstan across the gorge and fixed into the masonry on either side. A basket was slung from it to enable men and materials to cross the gorge. The force of gravity took it down to the centre, from where it was hauled up to the other side with a rope. In the 1850s, when work was temporarily abandoned, people paid considerable sums for the dubious pleasure of travelling from Clifton Down to Leigh Woods the adventurous way.

LEFT
An 1845 view painted by J. Fagan, showing the two piers all but abandoned. Fifteen more years were to elapse before the bridge's fortunes were to change.

The road level of Clifton Suspension Bridge is 1m (3 feet) higher at the Clifton end than at the Leigh Woods end. Brunel incorporated this into the design to give the bridge the appearance of being absolutely horizontal.

RIGHT
Old Hungerford Bridge, built by Brunel in 1845. When it was dismantled in 1862, its chains were re-used to complete Clifton Suspension Bridge.

FAR RIGHT
Clifton Suspension Bridge in August 1863. The temporary staging on which the eastern chains were to be laid is in place.

IN 1857 an attempt was made to revive the Clifton bridge project when Lt. Col. Serrell, the designer of a bridge at Niagara, proposed a lighter, slightly cheaper bridge supported by wire ropes. Isambard Brunel was clearly unenthusiastic about the scheme and insufficient capital was forthcoming. So for three further years the bridge works remained unaltered.

The Principles of a Suspension Bridge

The weight of the deck is carried by the suspension rods. These pull down on the chain causing it to sag and to pull inwards at its ends. The downward force at each end is carried by the upwards resistance of the stone piers. To prevent the chain from pulling inwards, it has to be anchored in solid rock.

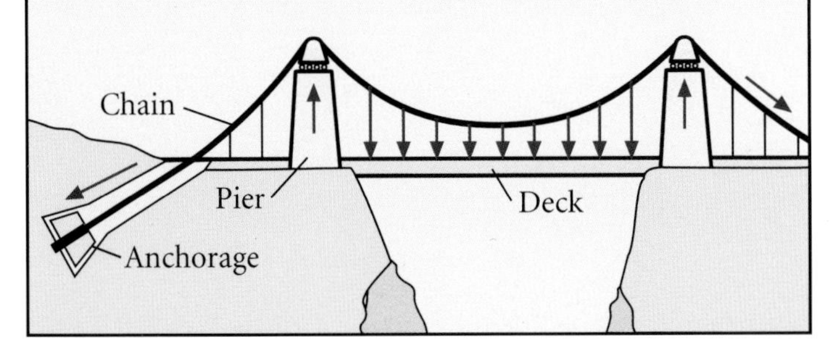

It was during this period that Brunel died. Ironically, his death was to inspire what in life he had so desired, yet had been unable to achieve – the completion of Clifton Suspension Bridge. Two factors brought this about. Firstly, the Institution of Civil Engineers required a fitting monument to their former colleague and expressed regret that the bridge that had been so dear to his heart should remain unfinished. Secondly, and by happy coincidence, Hungerford Bridge in London, which Brunel had built in the 1840s, was at the time due to make way for a new Charing Cross railway bridge. The Hungerford chains, almost the same as those designed for Clifton, were not only to be available but would require disposal.

Events moved very quickly. After an optimistic feasibility study, engineers W.H. Barlow and Sir John Hawkshaw, the designer of the Charing Cross bridge, brought the Clifton trustees and the engineers together. Soon, in May 1860, a new bridge company was formed. One difference between the new Clifton scheme and the old was an increase in deck width from 7.3m (24 feet) up to 9.2m (30 feet). The

To enable the construction of the temporary staging to begin, a light rope was passed from one bank to the other. One story has it that this was done by flying it across on a kite!

company estimated that around £45,000 would be necessary to see the project through. By December £30,000 of this had been raised. In June 1861, a new Act went through Parliament to confirm that the bridge scheme had truly come alive again.

In June 1862 work resumed in the hands of contractors Cochrane & Co. of Dudley. By November, the Hungerford chains were available. Tests with them made Hawkshaw and Barlow decide, for ease of adaptation, to use three chains instead of the two that Brunel had planned and to raise the bridge from 71m (230 feet) to 75m (245 feet) above the water. Also the amount of chain on the landward side of each pier was to be reduced. It was calculated that an additional 500 tons of chain would be needed and this was ordered. On 4 June 1863 the first wire was passed across the gorge, a new and permanent link between the towers which for so long had stood in grim isolation.

The Chains

The chains of Clifton Suspension Bridge are not chains as we usually think of them. Each section is made up of between 10 and 12 links of flat metal 7.6m (25 feet) long, like huge spanners with closed ends, placed side-by-side and bolted together through the end holes. To achieve the correct profile of the bridge's chains, the bottom chains were first joined up as single links and adjusted for shape. Only after this were all the parallel links added to each section. The design of the joints between the links is of critical importance in minimizing weight while maintaining strength. Modern computer analysis has revealed that Brunel's design was close to the ideal.

Right: The chain link connection.

ABOVE
The bridge in early summer 1864. Work on the deck is well advanced. The temporary staging and traveller wire can be clearly seen around the western (right) chains.

TO construct the chains that support the bridge, the first task was to sling a temporary bridge from one pier to another, similar to a rope bridge across a jungle river. Its footway was made up of six wire ropes planked across and bound with iron hoops. Two wire handrails made up the sides. At head height was another wire. On this ran the 'traveller', a light frame on wheels that carried each link of the chain out to the men in the middle. Besides being a walkway, the wire bridge acted as a staging on which the chain rested as new links were added, wooden blocks being placed beneath. To keep the temporary bridge secure in high winds, it was anchored by ropes to the rocks below.

By August 1862, this temporary bridge was in place and the enlarged anchorage tunnels were ready for the three chains that were to support each side. These were assembled link by link – up to 100 links per day, men working simultaneously from the anchorages at both sides of the gorge. When the first chain was complete, the second was built on top and then the third. When the three chains on the eastern (Bristol) side were finished, the walkway was dismantled and re-rigged for the western chains to be assembled.

When all the chains were complete, vertical suspension rods, 2.5m (8 feet) apart, were fastened to the chains by the bolts that joined the links together. To equalize the

The Saddles

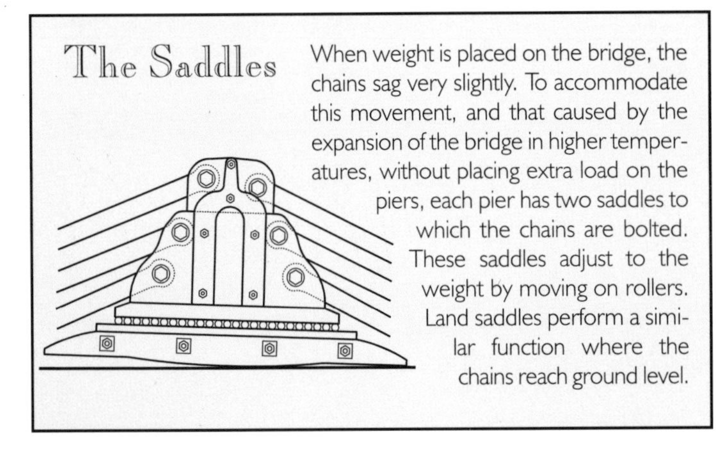

When weight is placed on the bridge, the chains sag very slightly. To accommodate this movement, and that caused by the expansion of the bridge in higher temperatures, without placing extra load on the piers, each pier has two saddles to which the chains are bolted. These saddles adjust to the weight by moving on rollers. Land saddles perform a similar function where the chains reach ground level.

The Anchorages

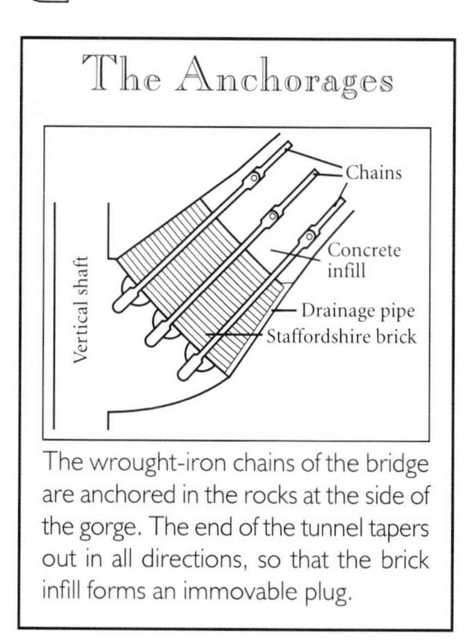

The wrought-iron chains of the bridge are anchored in the rocks at the side of the gorge. The end of the tunnel tapers out in all directions, so that the brick infill forms an immovable plug.

stress, each rod was fastened to only one of the chains: top, middle or bottom in turn. By 8 May 1864 all six chains were complete and ready for the deck to be suspended below it.

The main strength of the deck comes from two huge girders that run the full length of the bridge, visible to us as the division between the roadway and the footpath. To build these over a 75m (245-foot) drop, the contractors used two long-jibbed cranes, one at each side, to move 5m (16-foot) sections into a position where they could be attached to the suspension rods by bolted plates. As soon as two parallel sections were fitted, cross-girders were bolted beneath them at right angles to form a rigid structure. These were then boarded over temporarily so that the crane could move on. Behind the cranes on each side the floor of the roadway was put in place, using interlocking sleepers of 13cm (5-inch) Baltic timber. Over this, at right angles, a layer of timber about 5cm (2 inches) thick was laid. On 2 July 1864, the last cross-girder was fixed in the centre of the bridge. By the end of August, work on the painting, approach roads and toll houses was nearly completed. As a safety test, 500 tons of stone were spread on the road and footpaths. The bridge sagged 18cm (7 inches) in the middle, well within acceptable tolerances. The Clifton Suspension Bridge was ready for its grand opening.

ABOVE
Purely as a precaution, in 1925 and 1939 the anchorages were reinforced by extra chains and the tunnels filled to a 6m (20-foot) depth with concrete.

LEFT
The bridge in late June 1864. The deck is almost ready to be crossed for the first time.

The first recorded suspension bridges were built in China around AD550.

The first suspension bridge in Britain was a 1741 chain footbridge over the River Tees, Co. Durham.

The first metal suspension bridge was built in 1809 over the Merrimac River, Massachusetts, USA.

The first major suspension bridge in Europe was built in 1826 by Thomas Telford over the Menai Straits to connect Anglesey with the Welsh mainland.

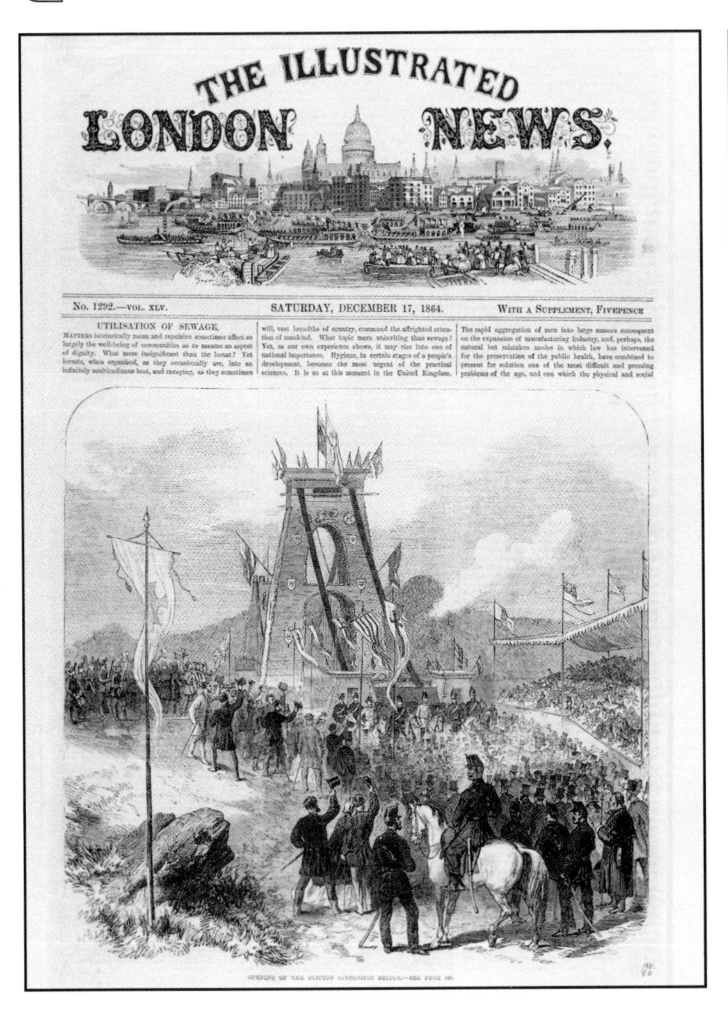

THE ILLUSTRATED LONDON NEWS.

No. 1292.—VOL. XLV. SATURDAY, DECEMBER 17, 1864. WITH A SUPPLEMENT, FIVEPENCE

UTILISATION OF SEWAGE.

MATTERS intrinsically mean and repulsive sometimes affect so largely the well-being of communities as to assume an aspect of dignity. What more insignificant than the locust? Yet locusts, when organised, as they occasionally are, into an infinitely multitudinous host, and ravaging, as they sometimes will, vast breadths of country, command the affrighted attention of mankind. What topic more uninviting than sewage! Yet, as our own experience shows, it may rise into one of national importance. Hygiene, in certain stages of a people's development, becomes the most urgent of the practical sciences. It is so at this moment in the United Kingdom. The rapid aggregation of men into large masses consequent on the expansion of manufacturing industry, and, perhaps, the natural but mistaken modes in which law has intervened for the preservation of the public health, have combined to present for solution one of the most difficult and pressing problems of the age, and one which the physical and social

The Latin motto on the Clifton pier – 'Suspensa vix via fit' – means, loosely translated, 'A suspended way made with difficulty'. It is thought to be a pun on the name of William Vick, the bridge's founder.

ABOVE
An elaborate engraving from *The Illustrated London News* conveys the great excitement in Bristol on the day of the bridge's opening.

RIGHT
A ticket for a horse-drawn carriage from the early days of the bridge.

THE ceremonial opening of Clifton Suspension Bridge on 8 December 1864 was indeed very grand, reflecting the pride and delight of Bristol people that all problems had been overcome and a very fine bridge built. Although no member of the Royal Family could be present, in an attempt to make up for this the authorities pulled out all the stops to make the occasion a truly memorable one.

Despite heavy rain the night before, the day was fine and at 10 a.m. a long procession started out from the city centre amid huge crowds. Her Majesty's forces led the parade with five different army regiments and the Royal Navy represented. Military horses pulled the six field guns that were to fire the salute. Behind the troops marched groups with their banners representing the many trades, organizations and friendly societies of the city. At least 16 bands accompanied the procession as it wound its way through packed and cheering streets up to Clifton.

At a Clifton hotel, the assembled guests (who included foreign consuls, clergy, MPs, magistrates, councillors and peers of the realm) joined the final approach to the bridge. Every inch of the heights with a view of the proceedings was crammed with spectators. Flags and banners flew and church bells rang. Triumphal arches had been erected and the piers of the bridge were elaborately decorated with flowers and greenery. A military guard lined the route as, at midday, the procession moved on to the bridge.

After the ceremonial first crossing, the field guns fired a salute at the Leigh Woods

A786 A786
Clifton Suspension Bridge.
CARRIAGE TICKET.
CLEARANCE TICKET for Carriage not being a Public Conveyance for Passengers for Hire.
Available for day of issue only.
J. G. DENNEHY, Secretary.

end and the procession returned to the Clifton side. On a dais in front of a grandstand various dignitaries gave addresses, amongst them Captain Huish, chairman of the bridge company. The Bishop of Bristol said prayers and fittingly, the two Lords Lieutenant of Somerset and Gloucestershire formally opened the bridge. Cheers were given for the engineers, and the National Anthem was played.

After the ceremony, the invited guests retired to a banquet at the Victoria Rooms while the crowds stayed on well into the evening to see the bridge illuminated.

Opening of Clifton Suspension Bridge.

SUSPENSA VIX VIA FIT

BANQUET AT THE VICTORIA ROOMS,
THURSDAY 8TH DECEMBER 1864.
At 4.30. o'Clock precisely.
IN CELEBRATION OF THE
Opening of the Bridge on that Day.
Ladies Ticket.

No 174

Chairman.

ABOVE
Crowds await the procession from the city at the opening ceremonial on 8 December 1864.

LEFT
A ticket to the celebration banquet which followed the grand opening.

FAR LEFT
A glass tankard made to commemorate the bridge's 125th anniversary.

ABOVE
Bridge maintenance men walk the chains in the days when safety precautions were less stringent.

RIGHT
A maintenance worker inspects one of the tunnels at the north end of the bridge.

TODAY Clifton Suspension Bridge is looked after by a Trust set up under a Parliamentary Act of 1952. The 13 trustees include representatives of local authorities together with others chosen for their technical or business expertise. The trustees are empowered to collect tolls, although since 1991 pedestrians and bicycles have crossed free of charge. The toll money goes mainly to meet the regular costs of staffing, repairs and maintenance.

Day-to-day responsibility for the bridge is in the hands of the Bridge Master who is on call 24 hours a day. Under him is a staff of 13 tollkeepers and four maintenance men.

The toll charge also contributes to the illumination of the bridge. Ever since its opening, the bridge has been lit regularly, although there was keen disappointment on that first night in 1864 when magnesium flares on the roadway kept blowing out and had to be discarded. In the 1930s big events came to be celebrated by large numbers of

Engineers Hawkshaw and Barlow used wrought-iron plate girders and lattice cross girders for the structure of the deck. Brunel had specified a timber framework with iron straps which would not have lasted so well. Some of Brunel's timber and iron viaducts elsewhere have not survived.

electric lights. For the bridge's centenary in 1964, it was illuminated with 4,000 bulbs and for the Queen's Silver Jubilee in 1977 it was floodlit. Any surplus of toll money above routine expenditure is set aside for large-scale repairs that might be needed and to subsidize future toll levels.

Clifton Suspension Bridge is very much the same structure as it was in 1864. To make this possible, it is thoroughly examined twice a year and from time to time major repairs are carried out. The chain anchorages were strengthened in 1925 and 1939 and the timber beneath the road entirely renewed in 1958–59. The ironwork, originally coated with coal tar and later with special paints, is now protected by a zinc coating beneath the paint, applied in the mid-1950s and renewed as need arises.

Work below the road deck is done from a motorized cradle slung beneath the bridge. Access to the suspension rods is from a bosun's chair fastened to the chains and hoisted aloft by hand. For safety, workmen working on top of the chains wear a harness that is clipped to a wire running centrally up the chains.

It is remarkable that whenever developments in technology, such as fibre optics, allow engineers to look at previously hidden parts of the structure or to test it in some new way, the condition of the bridge is always surprisingly good – a tribute both to Brunel, Hawkshaw and Barlow for the quality of their design and to the many generations of trustees and maintenance people who have looked after the bridge so well.

The design of Clifton Suspension Bridge becomes even more remarkable when one considers it was built to carry carriage traffic, pedestrians and animals, yet can cope with today's vehicles of up to 4 tons in weight. This durability is due in large part to the iron parapet on the outside of each footway which gives added stiffness and strength.

ABOVE
Throughout the year, a maintenance team keeps the bridge in good repair. Every six months the structure of the bridge is examined by a firm of consulting engineers.

LEFT
As part of the continuous programme of maintenance, a workman attends to the bridge's security lighting.

By Night and Day

ABOVE
Clifton Suspension Bridge is one of the finest sights in Britain, particularly when illuminated at night.

RIGHT
In 1989 fireworks celebrated the 125th anniversary of the bridge's opening.

IN recent years Clifton Suspension Bridge has been lit nightly, but in 1991 faults in the elderly wiring caused the trustees to seek a more modern and effective lighting system. The strings of individual 'fairy lights', to be seen in the 1989 picture (left), were replaced by illuminated strips down the suspension rods. Even though today's lighting is much more reliable than the flares which blew out at the 1864 opening ceremony, the bridge's exposed position means that the maintenance staff wage a constant war against water penetration, in order to preserve every evening a marvellous spectacle and a memorable feature of the Bristol scene.

Each year between 3 and 4 million vehicles cross the bridge, with 3,000 Bristol commuters using it every weekday morning. July and August are the peak months. Sunday and Monday are the quiet days. In 1975 manual collection of tolls ceased when automatic barriers were installed.

LEFT
This old Wolseley crossing the bridge during an annual car rally echoes the many millions of now historic vehicles that the bridge has carried over the years.

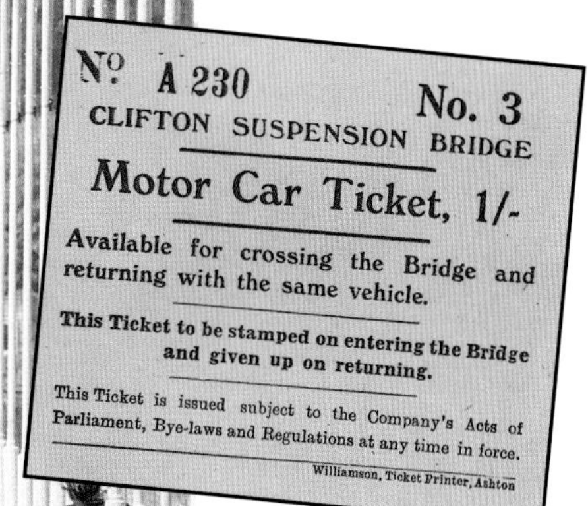
Nº A 230 No. 3
CLIFTON SUSPENSION BRIDGE
Motor Car Ticket, 1/-
Available for crossing the Bridge and returning with the same vehicle.
This Ticket to be stamped on entering the Bridge and given up on returning.
This Ticket is issued subject to the Company's Acts of Parliament, Bye-laws and Regulations at any time in force.
Williamson, Ticket Printer, Ashton

ABOVE
A motor vehicle ticket dating from the 1950s. Past tickets have catered for many types of bridge crosser – from sheep upwards.

A Stirring Sight

RIGHT
On a misty summer morning the bridge provides a stirring sight.

BELOW
The Lookout at Clifton was restored in 1994 by the Clifton and Hotwells Improvement Society, supported by the trustees, the City of Bristol and many public and private donors.

Some Facts

Total span	214m (702 feet)
Overall width	9.5m (31 feet)
Height above high water level	75m (245 feet)
Height of piers	26m (86 feet)
Total weight	1,500 tons
Number of links	4,200
	(7.6m (25 feet) x 18cm (7 inches) x 2.5cm (1 inch))
Number of suspension rods	162
	(1m (3 feet) to 20m (65 feet) long)

In 1885, a distressed young woman, Sarah Renley, jumped off the bridge. Her billowing skirts acted as a parachute and she landed gently in the river. Sarah lived happily into her seventies.

The first aeroplane to fly beneath Clifton Suspension Bridge was that of Frenchman M. Tetard in 1911. In spite of a later ban on such escapades, in 1957 Flying Officer J.G. Crossley of 501 Sqn at nearby Filton took his Vampire jet beneath the bridge at a speed of 450 mph, only to crash into the side of the gorge and perish in the fire that followed.